WWW.BENDOCKERY.COM

50 CHRISTMAS DUETS
VOLS. 1 - 5

CONTENTS

- JINGLE BELLS
- JOLLY OLD ST. NICHOLAS
- JOY TO THE WORLD
- LO, HOW A ROSE E'ER BLOOMING
- O COME ALL YE FAITHFUL
- O COME, O COME, EMMANUEL
- O HOLY NIGHT
- O LITTLE TOWN OF BETHLEHEM
- O TANNENBAUM (O CHRISTMAS TREE)
- ONCE IN ROYAL DAVID'S CITY
- SILENT NIGHT
- SING WE NOW OF CHRISTMAS
- STILL, STILL, STILL
- THE BIRTHDAY OF A KING
- THE FIRST NOEL
- THE FRIENDLY BEASTS
- THE HOLLY AND THE IVY
- THE SNOW LAY ON THE GROUND
- THE TWELVE DAYS OF CHRISTMAS
- TOYLAND
- UP ON THE HOUSETOP
- WASSAIL SONG
- WE THREE KINGS
- WE WISH YOU A MERRY CHRISTMAS
- WEXFORD CAROL
- WHAT CHILD IS THIS?
- WHILE SHEPHERDS WATCHED

All Through the Night

Score

Traditional Welsh
B. C. Dockery

Arr. ©2022

All Through the Night

Violin

Traditional Welsh
B. C. Dockery

All Through the Night

Cello

Traditional Welsh
B. C. Dockery

All Through the Night

Piano

Traditional Welsh
B. C. Dockery

Angels From the Realm of Glory

Score

Henry Smart

B. C. Dockery

Arr. ©2022

Angels From the Realm of Glory

Violin

Henry Smart
B. C. Dockery

Angels From the Realm of Glory

Cello

Henry Smart
B. C. Dockery

Angels From the Realm of Glory

Piano

Henry Smart
B. C. Dockery

Away in a Manger

James R. Murray
arr. B C Dockery

Away in a Manger

James R. Murray
arr. B C Dockery

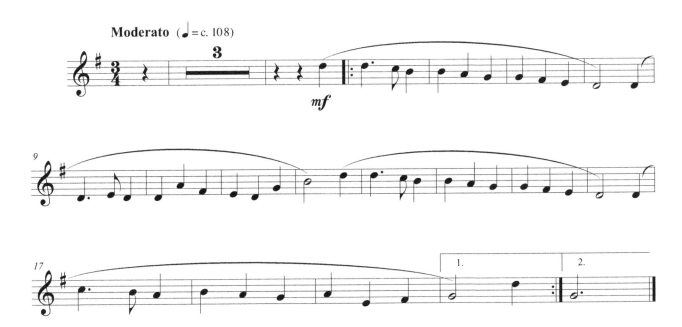

Away in a Manger

Cello

James R. Murray
arr. B C Dockery

Away in a Manger

Piano

James R. Murray
arr. B C Dockery

Away in a Manger (Cradle Song)

William J. Kirkpatrick
arr. B C Dockery

Away in a Manger (Cradle Song)

Away in a Manger (Cradle Song)

Violin

William J. Kirkpatrick
arr. B C Dockery

Away in a Manger (Cradle Song)

Cello

William J. Kirkpatrick
arr. B C Dockery

Away in a Manger (Cradle Song)

Piano

William J. Kirkpatrick
arr. B C Dockery

Bring a Torch, Jeanette Isabella

Score

Traditional French
B. C. Dockery

Arr. ©2022

Bring a Torch, Jeanette Isabella

Violin

Traditional French
B. C. Dockery

Bring a Torch, Jeanette Isabella

Cello

Traditional French
B. C. Dockery

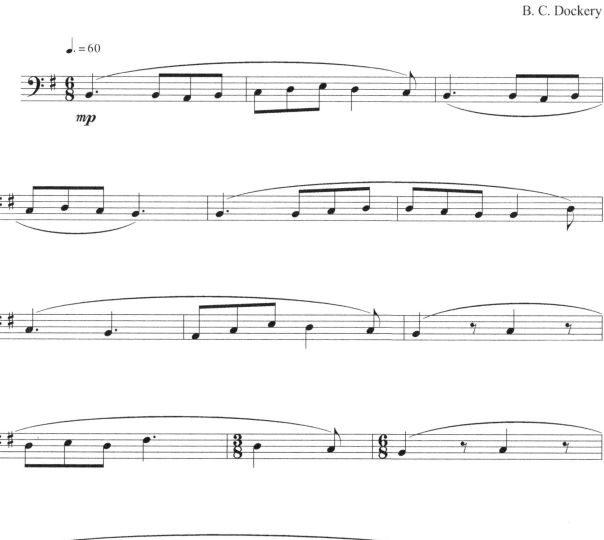

Bring a Torch, Jeanette Isabella

Piano

Traditional French
B. C. Dockery

Carol of the Bells

Mykola Leontovych
arr. B. C. Dockery

Carol of the Bells

Violin

Mykola Leontovych
arr. B. C. Dockery

Carol of the Bells

Cello

Mykola Leontovych
arr. B. C. Dockery

Carol of the Bells

Piano

Mykola Leontovych
arr. B. C. Dockery

Christ was Born on Christmas Day

Score

Traditional
B. C. Dockery

Arr. ©2022

Christ was Born on Christmas Day

Violin

Traditional
B. C. Dockery

Christ was Born on Christmas Day

Cello

Traditional
B. C. Dockery

Arr. ©2022

Christ was Born on Christmas Day

Piano

Traditional
B. C. Dockery

Christians, Awake

Score

John Wainwright
B. C. Dockery

Arr. ©2022

Christians, Awake

Christians, Awake

Violin

John Wainwright
B. C. Dockery

Arr. ©2022

Christians, Awake

Cello

John Wainwright
B. C. Dockery

Christians, Awake

Piano

John Wainwright
B. C. Dockery

Coventry Carol

Score

Traditional
B. C. Dockery

Coventry Carol

Violin

Traditional
B. C. Dockery

Arr. ©2022

Coventry Carol

Cello

Traditional
B. C. Dockery

Arr. ©2022

Coventry Carol

Piano

Traditional
B. C. Dockery

Dance of the Sugar Plum Fairy

Tchaikovsky
arr. B. C. Dockery

Dance of the Sugar Plum Fairy

Violin

Tchaikovsky
arr. B. C. Dockery

Cello

Dance of the Sugar Plum Fairy

Tchaikovsky
arr. B. C. Dockery

Piano

Dance of the Sugar Plum Fairy

Tchaikovsky
arr. B. C. Dockery

Deck the Halls

Old Welsh Air
arr. B. C. Dockery

Deck the Halls

Violin

Deck the Halls

Old Welsh Air
arr. B. C. Dockery

Cello

Deck the Halls

Old Welsh Air
arr. B. C. Dockery

Deck the Halls

Piano

Old Welsh Air
arr. B. C. Dockery

Ding Dong Merilly on High

Score

Traditional
B. C. Dockery

Arr. ©2022

Ding Dong Merilly on High

Violin

Traditional
B. C. Dockery

Ding Dong Merilly on High

Cello

Traditional
B. C. Dockery

Arr. ©2022

Ding Dong Merilly on High

Piano

Traditional
B. C. Dockery

Gaudete

Score

Traditional
B. C. Dockery

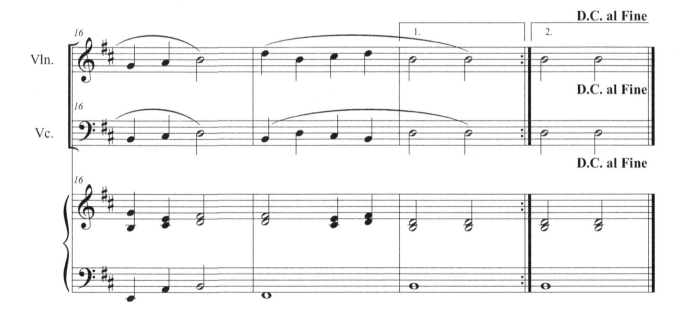

Gaudete

Violin

Traditional
B. C. Dockery

Gaudete

Cello

Traditional
B. C. Dockery

Arr. ©2022

Gaudete

Piano

Traditional
B. C. Dockery

Gesu Bambino

Score

Pietro Yon
B. C. Dockery

Gesu Bambino

Violin

Pietro Yon
B. C. Dockery

Gesu Bambino

Cello

Pietro Yon
B. C. Dockery

Arr. ©2022

Gesu Bambino

Piano

Pietro Yon
B. C. Dockery

God Rest Ye Merry Gentlemen

Traditional
arr. B. C. Dockery

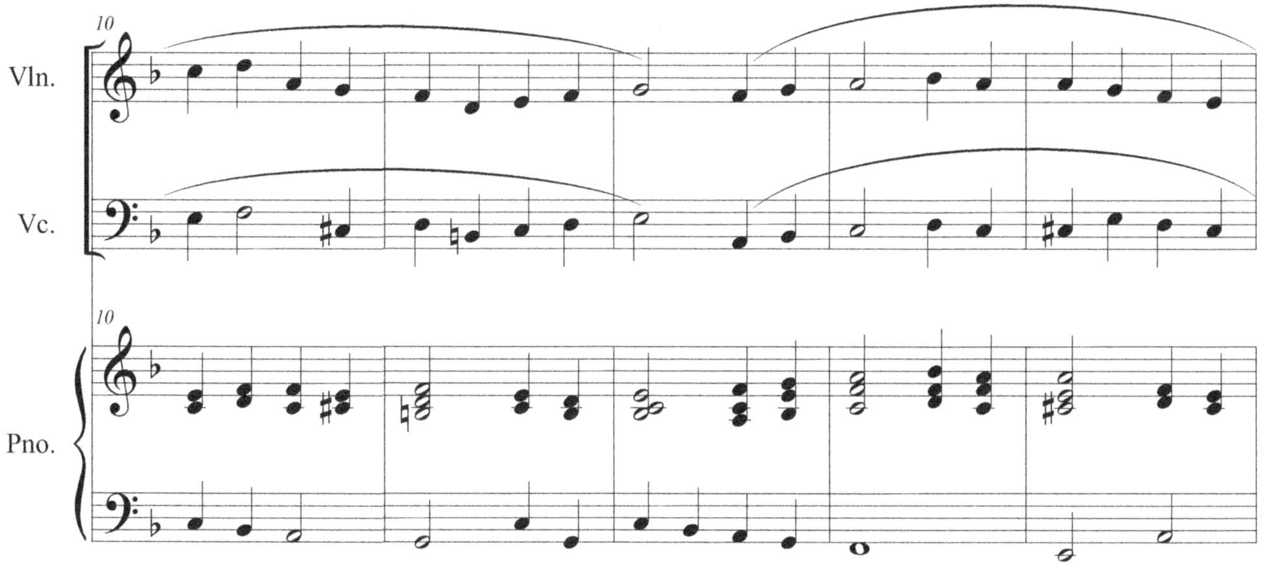
10
Vln.
Vc.
10
Pno.

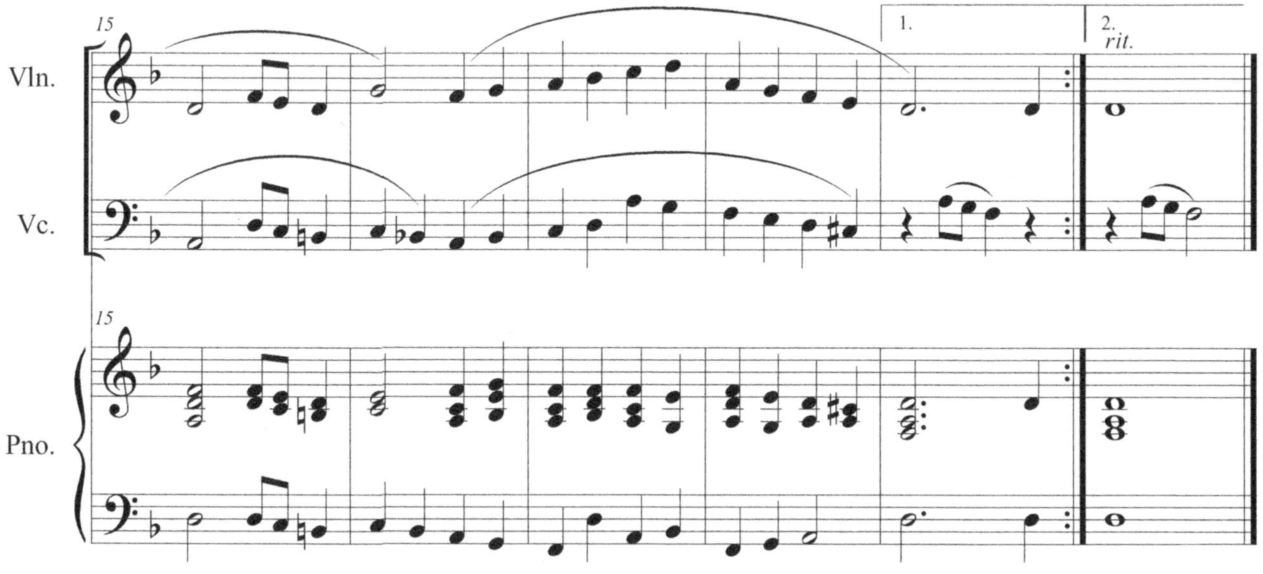
15
Vln.
1.
2.
rit.
Vc.
15
Pno.

God Rest Ye Merry Gentlemen

Violin

Traditional
arr. B. C. Dockery

Cello

God Rest Ye Merry Gentlemen

Traditional
arr. B. C. Dockery

God Rest Ye Merry Gentlemen

Piano

Traditional
arr. B. C. Dockery

Good Christian Men, Rejoice!

Score

Traditional German
B. C. Dockery

Good Christian Men, Rejoice!

Violin

Traditional German
B. C. Dockery

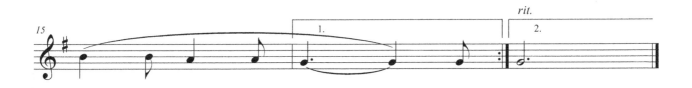

Arr. ©2022

Good Christian Men, Rejoice!

Cello

Traditional German
B. C. Dockery

Good Christian Men, Rejoice!

Piano

Traditional German
B. C. Dockery

Good King Wenceslas

Traditional
arr. B. C. Dockery

Allegro (M.M. ♩ = c. 120)

Good King Wenceslas

Good King Wenceslas

Violin

Traditional
arr. B. C. Dockery

Allegro (M.M. ♩= c. 120)

©2021

Cello

Good King Wenceslas

Traditional
arr. B. C. Dockery

Good King Wenceslas

Piano

Traditional
arr. B. C. Dockery

Hark, the Herald Angels Sing

Felix Mendelssohn
arr. B. C. Dockery

Hark, the Herald Angels Sing

Violin

Felix Mendelssohn
arr. B. C. Dockery

Cello
Hark, the Herald Angels Sing

Felix Mendelssohn
arr. B. C. Dockery

Hark, the Herald Angels Sing

Piano

Felix Mendelssohn
arr. B. C. Dockery

I Heard the Bells on Christmas Day

Jean Baptiste Calkin
arr. B. C. Dockery

I Heard the Bells on Christmas Day

Violin

Jean Baptiste Calkin
arr. B. C. Dockery

I Heard the Bells on Christmas Day

Cello

Jean Baptiste Calkin
arr. B. C. Dockery

I Heard the Bells on Christmas Day

Piano

Jean Baptiste Calkin
arr. B. C. Dockery

I Saw Three Ships

Traditional English
arr. B. C. Dockery

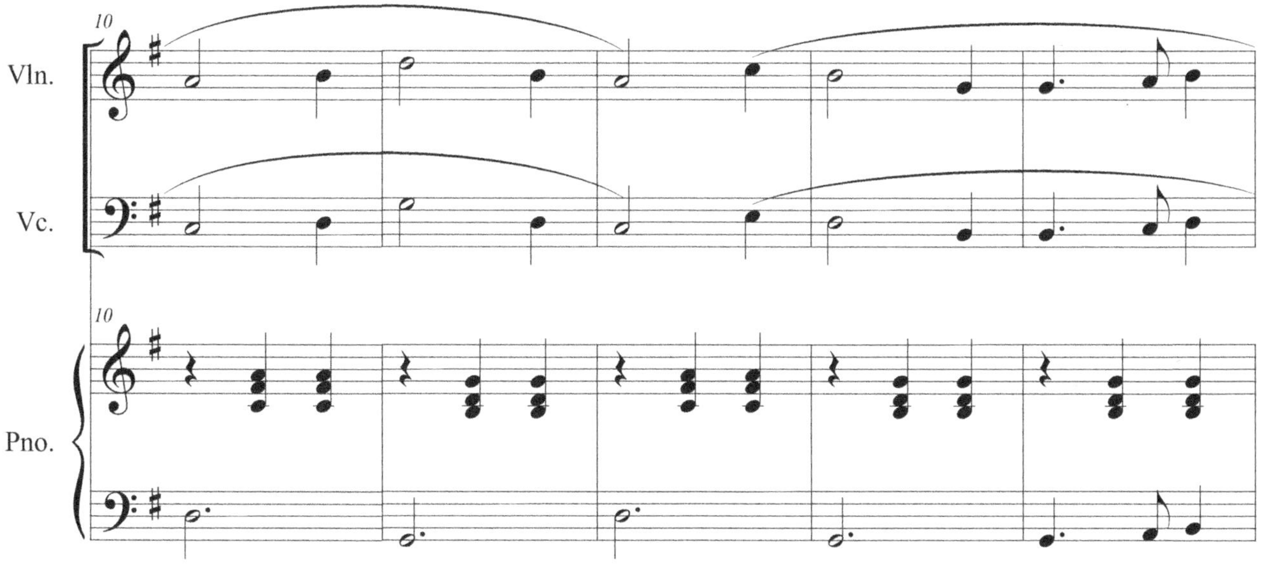
10
Vln.
Vc.
10
Pno.

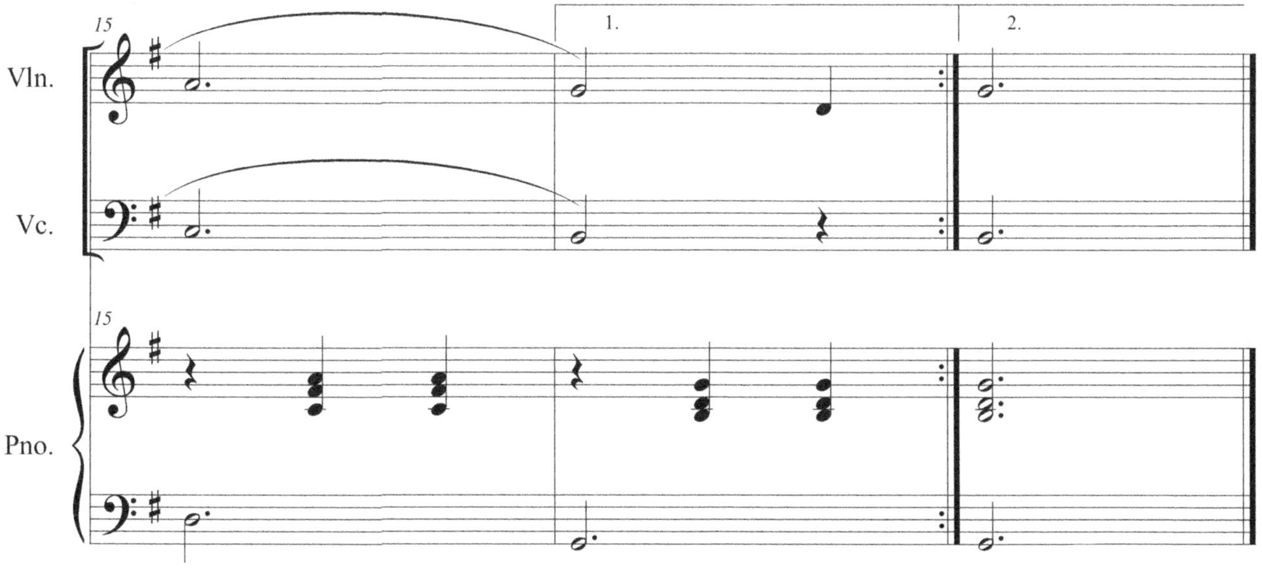
15
1.
2.
Vln.
Vc.
15
Pno.

I Saw Three Ships

Violin

Traditional English
arr. B. C. Dockery

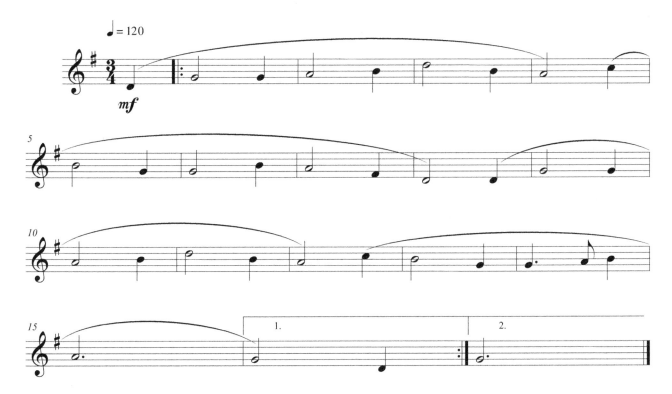

I Saw Three Ships

Cello

Traditional English
arr. B. C. Dockery

I Saw Three Ships

Piano

Traditional English
arr. B. C. Dockery

In the Bleak Midwinter

Gustav Holst
arr. B. C. Dockery

In the Bleak Midwinter

In the Bleak Midwinter

Violin

Gustav Holst
arr. B. C. Dockery

In the Bleak Midwinter

Cello

Gustav Holst
arr. B. C. Dockery

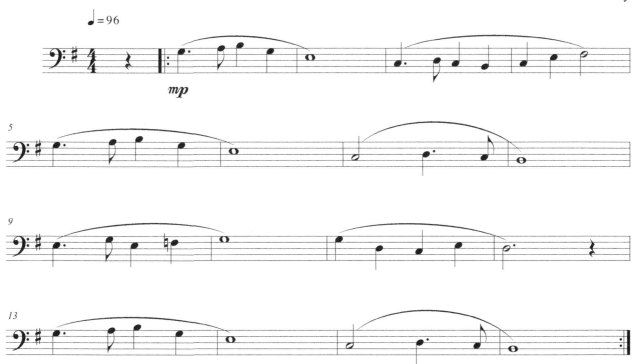

In the Bleak Midwinter

Piano

Gustav Holst
arr. B. C. Dockery

Infant Holy, Infant Lowly

Polish Carol
arr. B. C. Dockery

Infant Holy, Infant Lowly

Violin

Polish Carol
arr. B. C. Dockery

Infant Holy, Infant Lowly

Cello

Polish Carol
arr. B. C. Dockery

Infant Holy, Infant Lowly

Piano

Polish Carol
arr. B. C. Dockery

It Came Upon the Midnight Clear

Richard Storrs Willis
arr. B. C. Dockery

It Came Upon the Midnight Clear

It Came Upon the Midnight Clear

Violin

Richard Storrs Willis
arr. B. C. Dockery

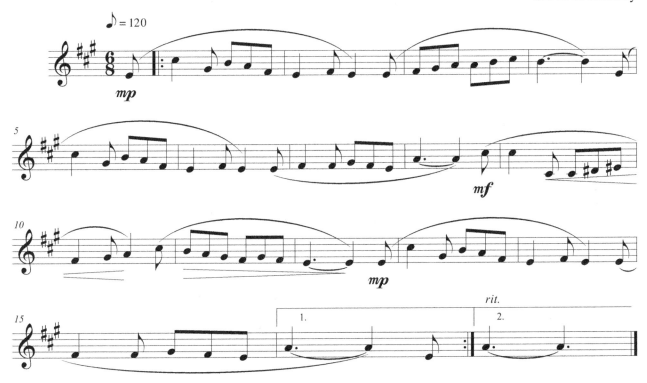

It Came Upon the Midnight Clear

Cello

Richard Storrs Willis
arr. B. C. Dockery

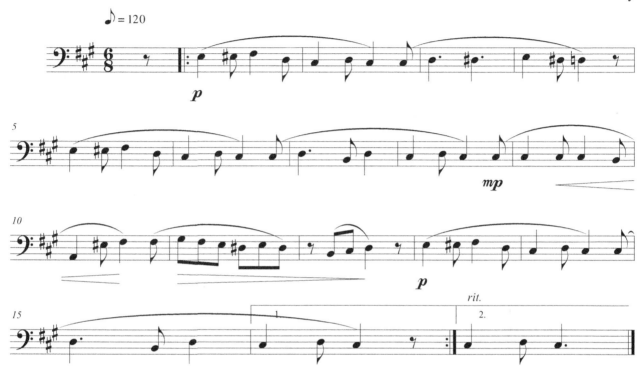

It Came Upon the Midnight Clear

Piano

Richard Storrs Willis
arr. B. C. Dockery

Jingle Bells

James Pierpont
arr. B C Dockery

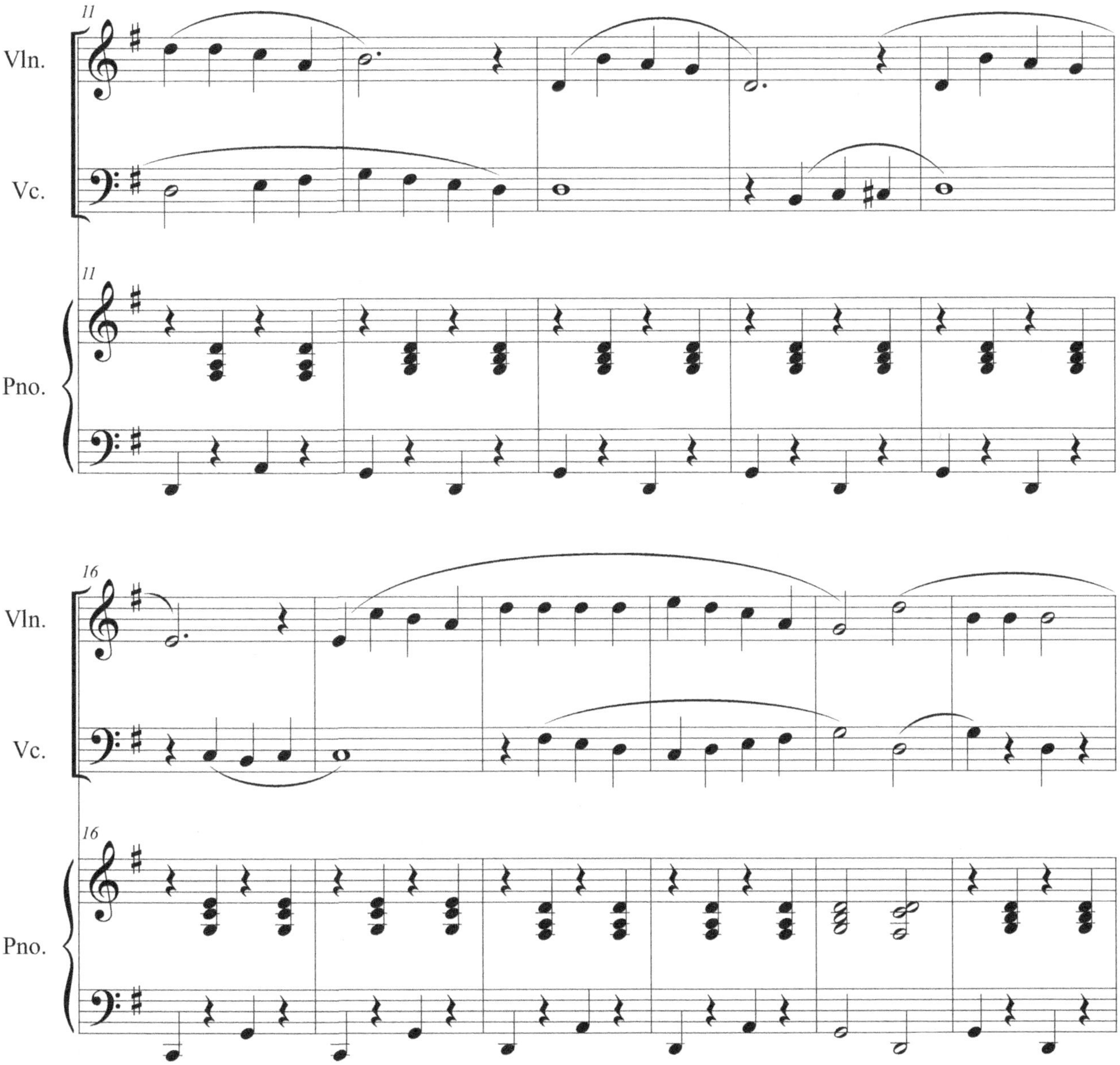
11
Vln.
Vc.
11
Pno.
16
Vln.
Vc.
16
Pno.

Jingle Bells

Jingle Bells

Violin

James Pierpont
arr. B C Dockery

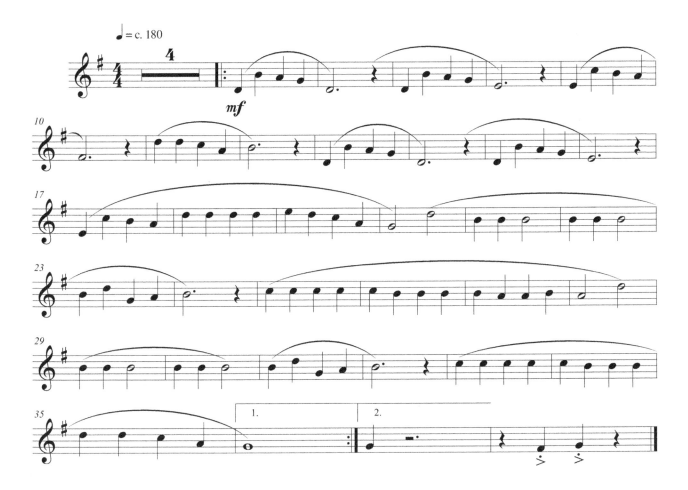

Jingle Bells

Cello

James Pierpont
arr. B C Dockery

Jingle Bells

Piano

James Pierpont
arr. B C Dockery

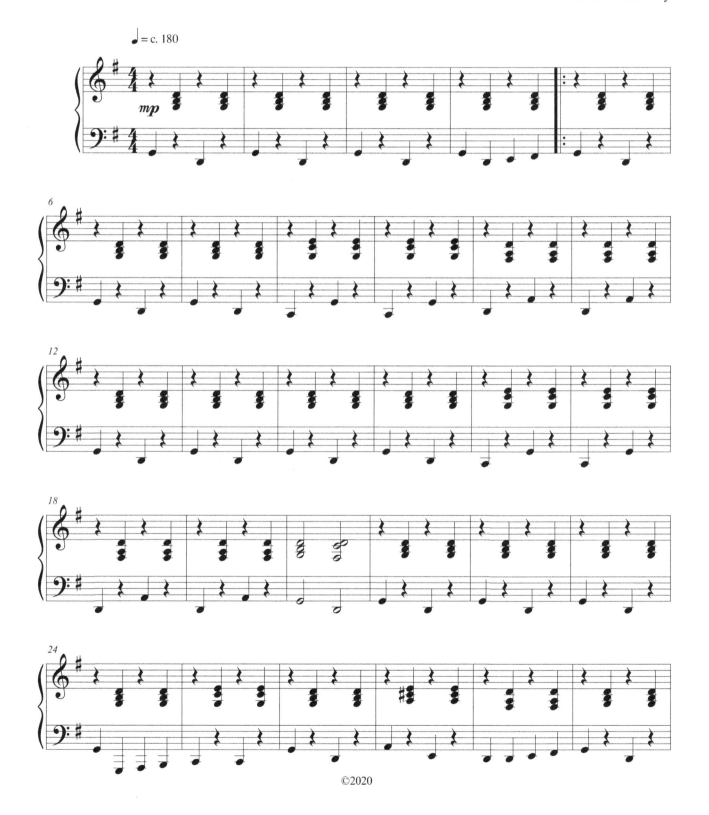

Jingle Bells

Jolly Old St. Nicholas

James R. Murray
arr. B. C. Dockery

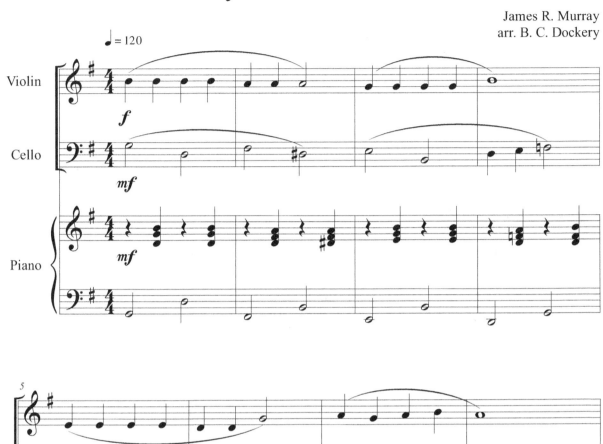

Jolly Old St. Nicholas

Violin

Jolly Old St. Nicholas

James R. Murray
arr. B. C. Dockery

Cello

Jolly Old St. Nicholas

James R. Murray
arr. B. C. Dockery

Jolly Old St. Nicholas

Piano

James R. Murray
arr. B. C. Dockery

Joy to the World

Handel
arr. B C Dockery

Joy to the World

Violin

Handel
arr. B C Dockery

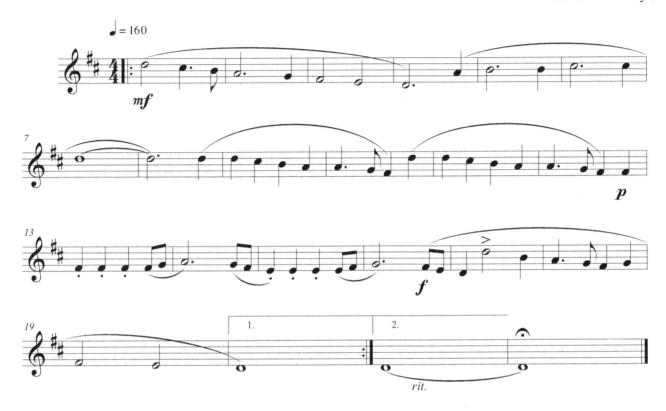

Cello

Joy to the World

Handel
arr. B C Dockery

Joy to the World

Piano

Handel
arr. B C Dockery

Lo, How a Rose E'er Blooming

Score

Traditional
B. C. Dockery

Lo, How a Rose E'er Blooming

Violin

Traditional
B. C. Dockery

Lo, How a Rose E'er Blooming

Cello

Traditional
B. C. Dockery

Arr. ©2022

Lo, How a Rose E'er Blooming

Piano

Traditional
B. C. Dockery

O Come All Ye Faithful

John Francis Wade
arr. B C Dockery

Allegro (M.M. ♩ = c. 120)

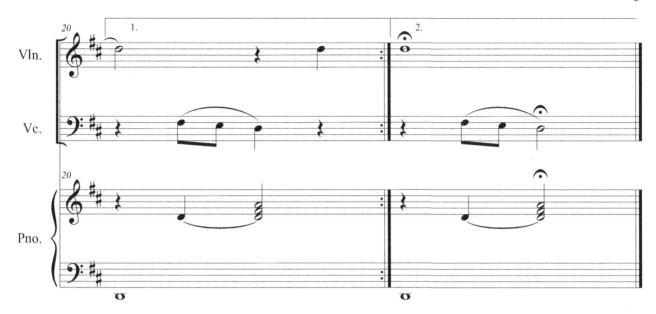

O Come All Ye Faithful

Violin

John Francis Wade
arr. B C Dockery

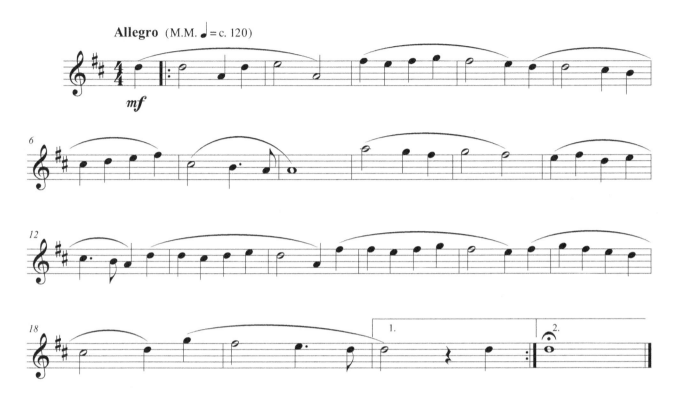

Cello

O Come All Ye Faithful

John Francis Wade
arr. B C Dockery

O Come All Ye Faithful

Piano

John Francis Wade
arr. B C Dockery

O Come, O Come, Emmanuel

Plainsong
arr. B. C. Dockery

O Come, O Come, Emmanuel

Violin

Plainsong
arr. B. C. Dockery

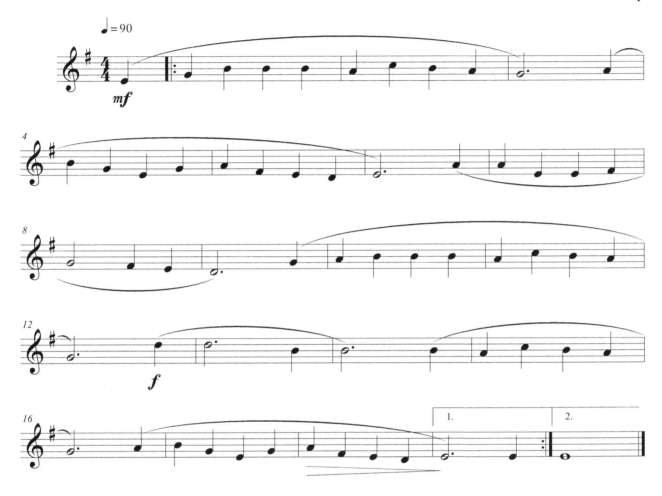

Cello

O Come, O Come, Emmanuel

Plainsong
arr. B. C. Dockery

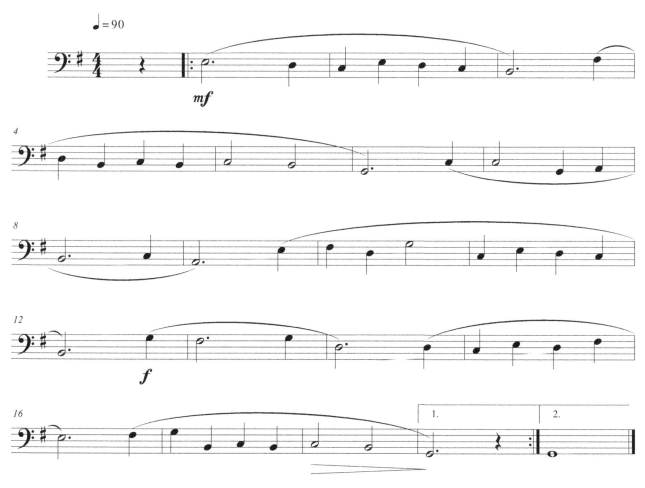

O Come, O Come, Emmanuel

Piano

Plainsong
arr. B. C. Dockery

O Holy Night

Adolphe Adam
arr. B C Dockery

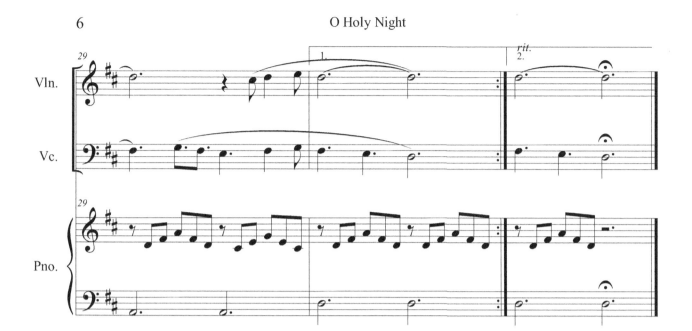

Violin

O Holy Night

Adolphe Adam
arr. B C Dockery

O Holy Night

Cello

Adolphe Adam
arr. B C Dockery

O Holy Night

Piano

Adolphe Adam
arr. B C Dockery

O Holy Night

O Little Town of Bethlehem

Lewis H. Redner
arr. B. C. Dockery

O Little Town of Bethlehem

Violin

Lewis H. Redner
arr. B. C. Dockery

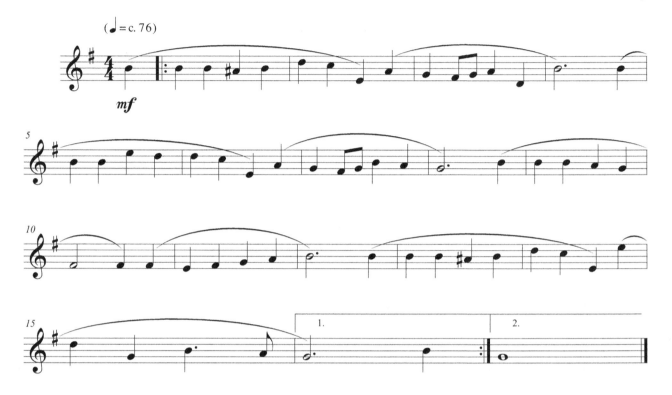

O Little Town of Bethlehem

Cello

Lewis H. Redner
arr. B. C. Dockery

O Little Town of Bethlehem

Piano

Lewis H. Redner
arr. B. C. Dockery

O Christmas Tree

O Tannenbaum

Traditional German
B. C. Dockery

O Christmas Tree

O Christmas Tree

O Tannenbaum

Violin

Traditional German
B. C. Dockery

O Christmas Tree

O Tannenbaum

Cello

Traditional German
B. C. Dockery

O Christmas Tree

O Tannenbaum

Piano

Traditional German
B. C. Dockery

Once in Royal David's City

Henry J. Gauntlett
arr. B. C. Dockery

Once in Royal David's City

Violin

Henry J. Gauntlett
arr. B. C. Dockery

Cello

Once in Royal David's City

Henry J. Gauntlett
arr. B. C. Dockery

Once in Royal David's City

Piano

Henry J. Gauntlett
arr. B. C. Dockery

Silent Night

Franz Gruber

Silent Night

Violin

Silent Night

Franz Gruber

Silent Night

Cello

Franz Gruber

Silent Night

Piano

Franz Gruber

Sing We Now of Christmas

French Carol
arr. B. C. Dockery

Sing We Now of Christmas

Violin

French Carol
arr. B. C. Dockery

Cello

Sing We Now of Christmas

French Carol
arr. B. C. Dockery

Sing We Now of Christmas

Piano

French Carol
arr. B. C. Dockery

Still, Still, Still

Traditional Austrian Carol
arr. B. C. Dockery

Still, Still, Still

Violin

Still, Still, Still

Traditional Austrian Carol
arr. B. C. Dockery

Still, Still, Still

Cello

Traditional Austrian Carol
arr. B. C. Dockery

Still, Still, Still

Piano

Traditional Austrian Carol
arr. B. C. Dockery

The Birthday of a King

Score

William Harold Neidlinger

B. C. Dockery

The Birthday of a King

The Birthday of a King

Violin

William Harold Neidlinger

B. C. Dockery

The Birthday of a King

Cello

William Harold Neidlinger
B. C. Dockery

Arr. ©2022

The Birthday of a King

Piano

William Harold Neidlinger
B. C. Dockery

The First Noel

Traditional
arr. B C Dockery

The First Noel

Violin

Traditional
arr. B C Dockery

The First Noel

Cello

Traditional
arr. B C Dockery

Piano

The First Noel

Traditional
arr. B C Dockery

The Friendly Beasts

Score

Pierre de Corbeil
B. C. Dockery

The Friendly Beasts

The Friendly Beasts

Violin

Pierre de Corbeil
B. C. Dockery

The Friendly Beasts

Cello

Pierre de Corbeil
B. C. Dockery

The Friendly Beasts

Piano

Pierre de Corbeil
B. C. Dockery

The Holly and the Ivy

Score

Traditional English
B. C. Dockery

The Holly and the Ivy

The Holly and the Ivy

Violin

Traditional English
B. C. Dockery

The Holly and the Ivy

Cello

Traditional English
B. C. Dockery

The Holly and the Ivy

Piano

Traditional English
B. C. Dockery

Arr. ©2022

The Snow Lay on the Ground

Score

Traditional
B. C. Dockery

Arr. ©2022

The Snow Lay on the Ground

Violin

Traditional
B. C. Dockery

The Snow Lay on the Ground

Cello

Traditional
B. C. Dockery

Arr. ©2022

The Snow Lay on the Ground

Piano

Traditional
B. C. Dockery

The Twelve Days of Christmas

Traditional English Carol
arr. B. C. Dockery

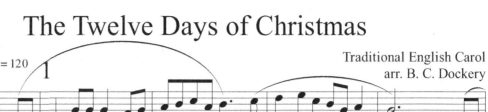

The Twelve Days of Christmas

6-12

repeat as needed

Repeat from 32 as needed

rit.

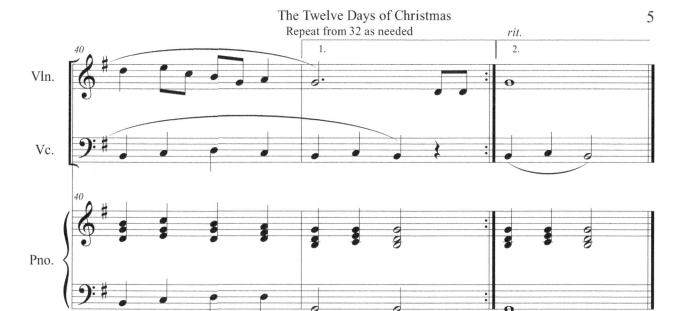

The Twelve Days of Christmas

Violin

Traditional English Carol
arr. B. C. Dockery

Cello

The Twelve Days of Christmas

Traditional English Carol
arr. B. C. Dockery

The Twelve Days of Christmas

Piano

Traditional English Carol
arr. B. C. Dockery

The Twelve Days of Christmas

Toyland

Score

Victor Herbert
B. C. Dockery

Toyland

Violin

Victor Herbert
B. C. Dockery

Arr. ©2022

Toyland

Cello

Victor Herbert
B. C. Dockery

Toyland

Piano

Victor Herbert
B. C. Dockery

Up on the Housetop

Score

Benjamin Hanby

B. C. Dockery

Arr. ©2022

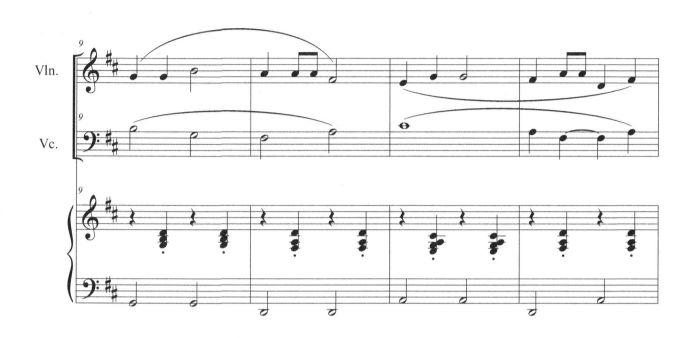

Up on the Housetop

Violin

Benjamin Hanby
B. C. Dockery

Up on the Housetop

Cello

Benjamin Hanby
B. C. Dockery

Arr. ©2022

Up on the Housetop

Piano

Benjamin Hanby
B. C. Dockery

Arr. ©2022

Here We Come A-Caroling

Wassail Song

Traditional English

B. C. Dockery

Arr. ©2022

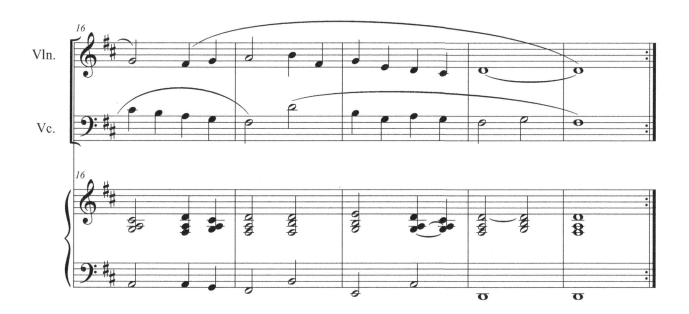

Here We Come A-Caroling

Violin

Wassail Song

Traditional English
B. C. Dockery

Arr. ©2022

2

Here We Come A-Caroling

Wassail Song

Cello

Traditional English
B. C. Dockery

Arr. ©2022

2

Here We Come A-Caroling

Wassail Song

Piano

Traditional English
B. C. Dockery

We Three Kings

John Henry Hopkins, Jr.
arr. B C Dockery

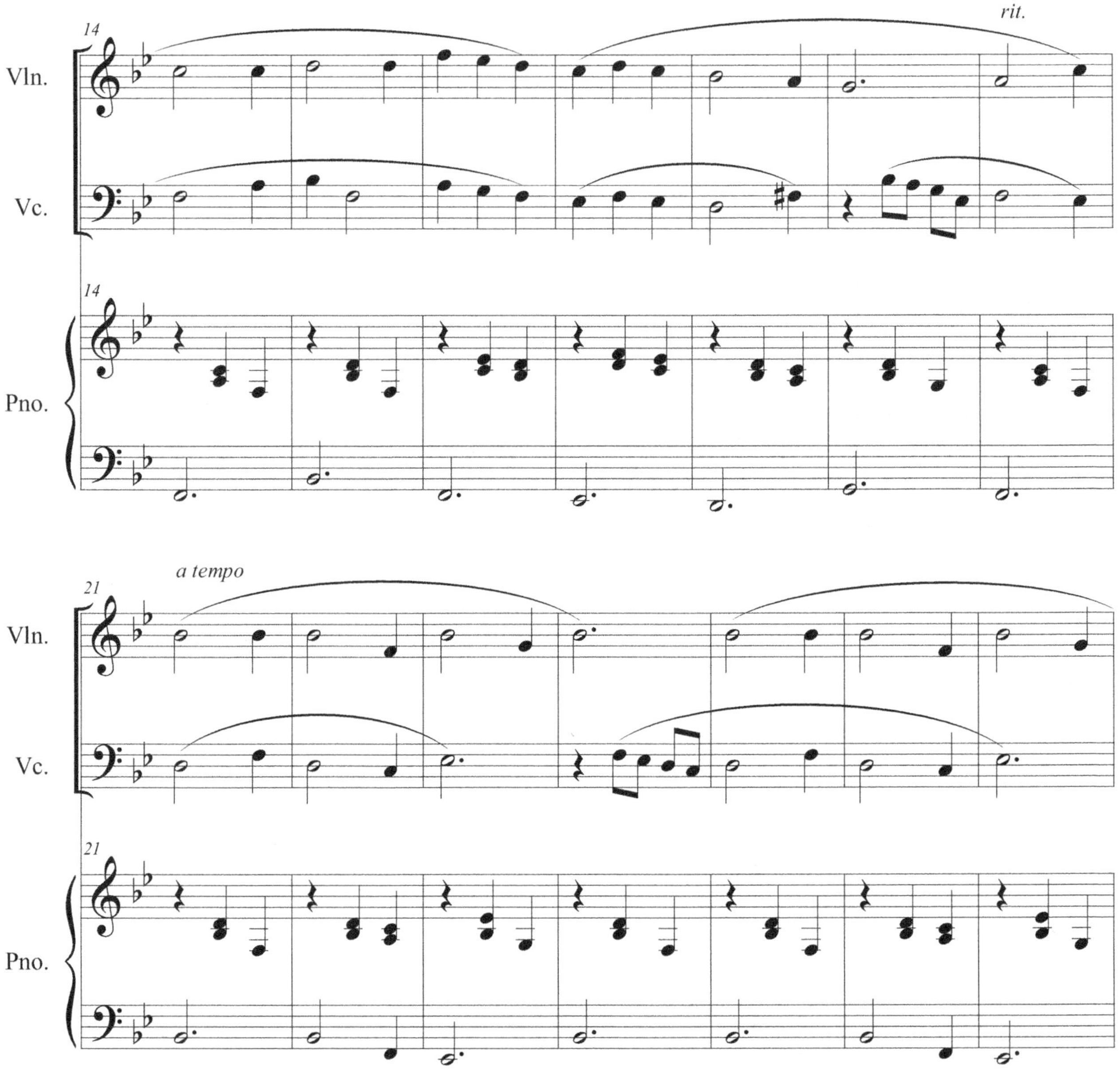
rit.
14
Vln.
Vc.
14
Pno.
a tempo
21
Vln.
Vc.
21
Pno.

We Three Kings

Violin

John Henry Hopkins, Jr.
arr. B C Dockery

Cello

We Three Kings

John Henry Hopkins, Jr.
arr. B C Dockery

We Three Kings

Piano

John Henry Hopkins, Jr.
arr. B C Dockery

©2020

We Wish You A Merry Christmas

Traditional English Carol
arr. B. C. Dockery

We Wish You A Merry Christmas

Violin

Traditional English Carol
arr. B. C. Dockery

We Wish You A Merry Christmas

Cello

Traditional English Carol
arr. B. C. Dockery

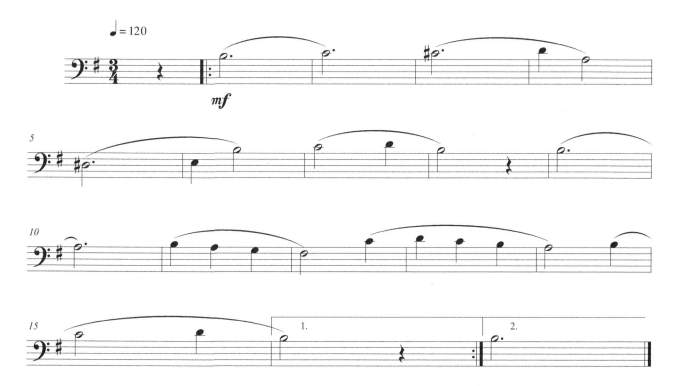

We Wish You A Merry Christmas

Piano

Traditional English Carol
arr. B. C. Dockery

The Wexford Carol

Traditional
arr. B. C. Dockery

Violin

The Wexford Carol

Traditional
arr. B. C. Dockery

Cello

The Wexford Carol

Traditional
arr. B. C. Dockery

The Wexford Carol

Piano

Traditional
arr. B. C. Dockery

What Child Is This (Greensleeves)

Traditional

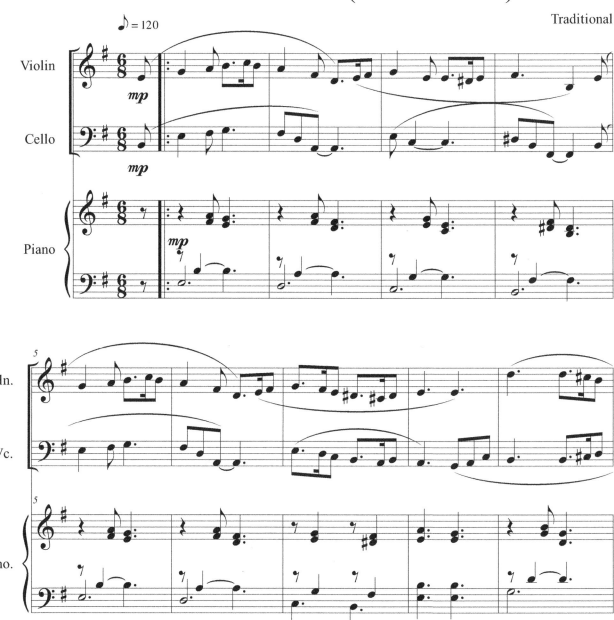

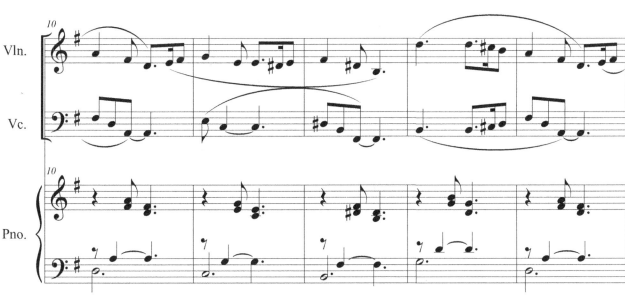

Violin

What Child Is This (Greensleeves)

Traditional

Cello

What Child Is This (Greensleeves)

Traditional

What Child Is This (Greensleeves)

Piano

Traditional

While Shepherds Watched Their Flock

Score

Nahum Tate
B. C. Dockery

While Shepherds Watched Their Flock

Violin

Nahum Tate
B. C. Dockery

While Shepherds Watched Their Flock

Cello

Nahum Tate
B. C. Dockery

While Shepherds Watched Their Flock

Piano

Nahum Tate
B. C. Dockery

Made in the USA
Las Vegas, NV
20 December 2024

14982284R00168